Sand Zoo

by Liza Charlesworth

ISBN: 978-1-338-78283-7
Illustrated by Kevin Zimmer
Copyright © 2021 by Liza Charlesworth. All rights reserved.
Published by Scholastic Inc., 557 Broadway, New York, NY 10012
10 9 8 7 6 5 4 3 2 1   68   21 22 23 24 25 26 27/0
Printed in Jiaxing, China. First printing, June 2021.

You can **use** sand
to make a lion.
Yahoo!

You can **use** sand
to make a penguin.
Yahoo!

You can **use** sand
to make a bear.
Yahoo!

You can **use** sand
to make a gorilla.
Yahoo!

5

You can **use** sand
to make a peacock.
Yahoo!

You can **use** sand
to make a kangaroo.
Yahoo!

You can **use** sand
to make a zoo.
Yahoo!

SAND
ZOO